NUMERICAL ABILITY FOR CEM

11+ NUMERACY WORKBOOK 1

Fully classroom-tested by Teachitright pupils and approved by parents

- Working with Numbers
- Equivalent Numbers
- Introduction to Algebra

University of Buckingham Press

Copyright information

Billy the Bookworm™ is the property of Teachitright

Authors

Chris Pearse

Jessica Hodge

The authors have asserted their moral rights under the Copyright, Designs and Patents Act, 1988, to be identified as the authors of this work.

First published in Great Britain in 2016 by

The University of Buckingham Press
Yeomanry House
Hunter Street
Buckingham MK18 1EG

A CIP catalogue record for this book is available at the British Library

ISBN 9781908684684

Teachitright

Teachitright is one of the most successful 11+ tuition companies in the South East. In the last 10 years we've supported thousands of pupils for both grammar school and independent school entry. We have 11 tuition centres across Buckinghamshire, Berkshire and Surrey.

Based on our wealth of experience and knowledge, we have produced a range of books that will help support your child through their 11+ journey in both CEM style and traditional 11+ tests and many Common Entrance exams. Our books, written by qualified teachers, have been classroom tested with pupils and adapted to ensure children are fully prepared and able to perform to the best of their ability.

Our unique mascot, Billy the Bookworm, will help guide children through the book and gives helpful hints and tips throughout.

We hope you find this book very useful and informative and wish you luck on your 11+ journey.

Teachitright holds a number of comprehensive revision courses and mock exams throughout the year. If you would like to find out more information, please visit:

www.teachitright.com

This Numerical Ability Workbook 1 alongside Workbook 2 provides the perfect preparation for both 11+ and Common Entrance exams. This book contains the key topics working with numbers, equivalent values and algebraic calculations. Workbook 2 contains data handling, shape and space and statistics.

How to use this book
As this book is broken down into **lessons** that cover different topics, it can be used to focus on individual areas of development or to work through every mathematical topic.

Learn: An informative teaching section to help with the key points and techniques for that lesson topic. It includes worked examples.

Develop: Opportunity to practise short calculations based on the lesson topic to ensure key principles and techniques are fully understood.

Timed tests: Strategically placed progressive timed tests to help build confidence with worded problems and time management.

The **answer section** gives detailed explanations to aid revision. There is also a **glossary** on page 70. It is important for the pupil to understand and learn keywords and phrases that are likely to appear in the exam.

In the back of the book is a **marking chart** and **progress grid** to help track your child's development throughout the topics and to highlight strengths and weaknesses.

Contents

SECTION 1:
WORKING WITH NUMBERS

Look out for Billy's tips and hints.

LEARN

Place value is a key element to all mathematics. In this first lesson you will grasp the main principles involved in understanding the value of a digit in a number. The value of a digit is determined by its place in relation to the position of the decimal point.

For example:

In Oliver's bank account he has £3465.00

The value of 3 is worth £3000, the value of 4 is worth £400, the value of 6 is worth £60

In Hannah's bank account she has £346.50 and the value of 3 is worth £300

In Alice's bank account she has £34.65 and the value of 3 is worth £30

The table below demonstrates the value of each digit.

3	2	1	5	6	7	8	9	1	.	2	3	5	4	8	1
THREE HUNDRED MILLION	TWENTY MILLION	ONE MILLION	FIVE HUNDRED THOUSAND	SIXTY THOUSAND	SEVEN THOUSAND	EIGHT HUNDRED	NINETY	ONE		TWO TENTHS	THREE HUNDREDTHS	FIVE THOUSANDTHS	FOUR TEN THOUSANDTHS	EIGHT HUNDRED THOUSANDTHS	ONE MILLIONTH

It is important to understand the value of decimals (that is, the digits written to the right of the decimal point).

For example: 3.476

4 is written one place to the right of the decimal point; so it has been divided by 10 or could be written as ⁴⁄₁₀ or 0.4

7 is written two places to the right of the decimal point; so it has been divided by 100 or could be written as ⁷⁄₁₀₀ or 0.07

6 is written three places to the right of the decimal point; so it has been divided by 1000 or could be written as ⁶⁄₁₀₀₀ or 0.006

DEVELOP

1) Using the number below, answer the following questions:

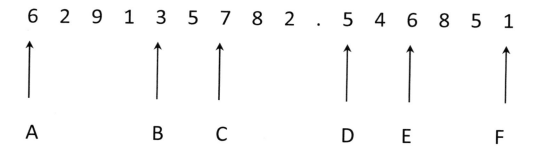

Write the value of the digits at:

A = 6   B = 3   C = 7   D = 5   E = 6   F = 1

2) Place the decimal point in the numbers below so that the number has:

i) 2 tens in it

a) 3621432

b) 72891 2

ii) 3 tenths in it

a) 46238 · 3

b) 23941 · 3

Rounding is when you write a number that isn't exact but you retain its **approximate values**. For example, 41 rounded to the nearest ten is 40. You may be asked to round (or rewrite) a number to the nearest ten, hundred, or thousand, or tenth, hundredth or thousandth. You may also be asked to round to one, two or three **decimal places** or to a number of **significant figures (SF)**. This lesson demonstrates how this is done.

Example one: Round 6825.9341 to the nearest thousand
Let's take you through the steps you need to make.

1) Identify the relevant digit and underline it.   **6̲845.9351**

2) Look to the right of that relevant digit and, if it is followed by a number which is 5 or more, you must round up. As it is followed by the digit 8, you must round up to the next thousand.
The rounded number is now 7000.

Example two: Rewrite 6845.9351 to the nearest tenth
Take the steps given in example one.
1) The relevant number is 9 tenths.   **6845.9̲351**

2) 9 is followed by a 3 so as 3 is less than 5 you do not round up, therefore it remains 9 tenths.
The rounded number to the nearest tenth is now 6845.9

Example three: Round 6845.9351 to two decimal places

1) The digit in the second decimal place is 3   **6845.93̲51**

2) 3 is followed by 5 so 3 is rounded up.
The rounded number is now 6845.94

Example four: Round 6845.9351 to two significant figures
Significant figures are used when we want a rough idea of a number or an approximation.
1) To round 6845.9351 to two significant figures you find the two most important numbers. The first most important number is 6 because it tells us the number is six thousand and something.

2) The second most significant number is 8. Remember to round up or down where required as in previous examples.
The number to two significant figures (SF) is 6800

DEVELOP

Try these rounding questions.

1) Rewrite 86734.287 to the nearest:

    a) hundred = 86700

    b) hundredth = 86734.290

    c) ten = 86734

    d) tenth = 86734.3

2) Rewrite 2864.37 to:

    a) one decimal place = 2864.4

    b) one significant figure =

    c) two significant figures =

3) Round 867.429 to the nearest:

    a) whole number =

    b) two decimal places =

    c) three significant figures =

5 or more, let it soar.

4 or less, let it rest.

TIMED TEST   *15 MINS*

Circle the letter above the correct answer with a pencil.

1) What is the correct value of the underlined digit? 2<u>3</u>5721.864

A	B	C	D	E
300	30	$\frac{3}{100}$	30000	300000

2) Help Nishaan to place a decimal point in the following number so that '4' has a value of four hundred: 6294165782

A	B	C	D	E
62.94165782	629416.5782	62941.65782	6294.165782	6.294165782

3) Alice was asked to select the biggest number in a maths quiz. Which should she select?

A	B	C	D	E
3678.9	3.6789	36.789	367.89	0.36789

4) What is the value of the underlined digit? 83.64<u>2</u>1

A	B	C	D	E
twenty	two	two thousand	two hundredths	two thousandths

5) Manreet was lent some money. She was asked to pay it back to the nearest ten pounds. £29452.95 was loaned to her. How much should she pay back?

A	B	C	D	E
£29000.95	£29400	£29450	£29452.90	£30000

6) The total number of people who attended a rock festival was 128468. What is this rounded to two significant figures?

A	B	C	D	E
100500	108000	100008	120000	130000

7) A range of mountain heights was given in a geography lesson. The children were asked to select the highest peak. Which height should they choose?

A	B	C	D	E
23402 ft	23042 ft	23420 ft	23024 ft	23204 ft

8) The fastest lap time in a motor race was 83.356 seconds. Write this to three significant figures.

A	B	C	D	E
83.4 secs	80.35 secs	83.3 secs	80.305 secs	83.006 secs

9) A box contains 48 tins of nails. Estimate the total number of tins in 731 boxes.

A	B	C	D	E
350	3500	35000	2800	28000

10) In humanities, Hannah was asked to research the Roman town of Colchester. The total population in 2014 was 186493. To assist her line graph construction she rounded the population to the nearest hundred. What was the rounded number?

A	B	C	D	E
186400	187490	186000	186500	190000

11) A factory produced 12356 cars in a month. What is this number to the nearest 10000?

A	B	C	D	E
10000	12000	110000	14000	13000

12) A shop sold 13963 shoes in a week. How many is this to the nearest 100?

A	B	C	D	E
13900	14000	13000	13600	14900

13) Oliver's student union, at university, in total collected 3456209kg of rubbish in a year. How much is this to the nearest hundred thousand?

A	B	C	D	E
3456200kg	3456000kg	3450000kg	3500200kg	3500000kg

14) Jovan was asked to write the number six hundred and five million five thousand and twenty seven. He got the number correct. Which number did he write?

A	B	C	D	E
605005027	650050027	655027	60005527	605050027

15) Jasveer is doing a sponsored drumming challenge and has to play his drums constantly for as long as possible. He plays for 1 hour 27 minutes and 32.478 seconds. What is his time to the nearest tenth of a second?

A	B	C	D	E
1h 27m 23.4s	1h 27m 20s	1h 30m 32.480s	1h 27m 30s	1h 27m 32.5s

LEARN

It is always useful to be able to recognise 'special' numbers. Included here are **prime numbers**, **square numbers**, **cube numbers** and **triangular numbers** as well as **odd numbers**, **even numbers** and **multiples**.

Many number sequences (a list of numbers) are made up of these 'special' numbers, so time could be saved very effectively by recognising, in both ascending and descending order, the number sequences.

PRIME NUMBERS: A prime number is a number with only two **factors**, itself and number one. The smallest prime number is 2, which is the only even number to be prime.

Here are the first 15 terms in the prime number sequence:

2, 3, 5, 7, 11, 13, 17, 19, 23, 29, 31, 37, 41, 43, 47

SQUARE NUMBERS: A square number is a number that results from a number that has been multiplied by itself. It is a whole number that has been raised to the power of 2.

For example:
The square number refers to the number of dots which are arranged in a square pattern. This can be shown below:

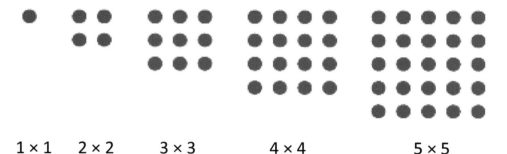

1×1 2×2 3×3 4×4 5×5

3 squared (or 3^2) = 3×3 = 9   so 9 is the square number.

Here are the first 15 terms in the square number sequence:

1, 4, 9, 16, 25, 36, 49, 64, 81, 100, 121, 144, 169, 196, 225

LEARN

CUBE NUMBERS: A cube number is a number which has been multiplied by itself three times. It is a whole number that has been raised to the power of 3.

For example:

2 cubed (or 2^3) is 2 × 2 × 2 = 8   so 8 is the cube number
4 cubed (or 4^3) is 4 × 4 × 4 = 64   so 64 is the cube number

Here are the first 15 terms in the cube number sequence:

1, 8, 27, 64, 125, 216, 343, 512, 729, 1000, 1331, 1728, 2197, 2744, 3375

TRIANGULAR NUMBERS: Like square numbers which can be illustrated in a square pattern, you can illustrate triangular numbers in two types of triangle patterns.

Whichever way you arrange the dots they make the same number sequence.

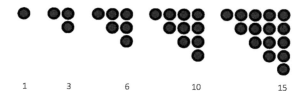

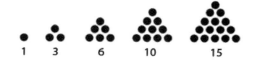

Here are the first 15 terms in the triangular number sequence:

1, 3, 6, 10, 15, 21, 28, 36, 45, 55, 66, 78, 91, 105, 120

Each time the difference in the terms goes up by 1

For example:
1 + 2 = 3
3 + 3 = 6
6 + 4 = 10

Other types of 'special' numbers could include odd numbers, even numbers and multiples.

LEARN

When you are given a number sequence, the first thing you should do is look to see whether you can recognise any of the 'special' numbers. If you cannot recognise the numbers as 'special', then calculate the difference between each number. You may then notice a pattern.

Example one:
6, 11, 16, 21, 26, 31

There is a '+ 5' between each number.

Example two:
3, 5, 6, 10, 9, 15, 12, 20, 15, 25, 18

This is called an alternate sequence because you can recognise multiples of 3 alternating with multiples of 5. Such sequences are often identified by their length: they are normally of longer length (that is, they have more terms) and the consecutive terms may increase and then decrease in value.

Example three:
 0, 1, 1, 2, 3, 5, 8, 13, 21, 34

A Fibonacci sequence is also important to recognise. This is when the previous two numbers have been added together to make the next number in the sequence and it starts with a zero or a 1

The numbers in a number sequence are called 'terms'.

DEVELOP

Fill in the three missing terms in each given sequence.

1)   16, 25, 36, 49, 64, ___ ___ ___

2)   7, 11, 13, 17, 19, ___ ___ ___

3)   225, 196, 169, 144, 121, ___ ___ ___

4)   1, ___ 27, ___ 125, ___

5)   8, 6, 16, 12, 24, 18, 32, ___ ___ ___

6)   1, 3, ___ 10, 15, ___ 28, ___

7)   81, 72, ___ 54, ___ 36, ___

8)   1, 1, 2, 3, 5, 8, ___ ___ ___

9)   4, 9, 19, 39, 79, ___ ___ ___

10)   960, 480, ___ 120, ___ 30, ___

Note down the differences between the sequences to help work out the link, for example:
2, (+2) 4, (+2) 6

LEARN

Introduction to the four maths operations

There are four main operations in maths. Like place value, their understanding is the foundation to all maths and calculations generally.

The operations are **addition**, **subtraction**, **multiplication** and **division**.

In order to understand and select what operation is being asked for, it is important that you are able to recognise the vocabulary used. The table below lists the common vocabulary associated with each operation:

ADDITION	SUBTRACTION	MULTIPLICATION	DIVISION
Add More Greater than Increase Plus Altogether Sum Total Perimeter	Subtract Takeaway Leave Decrease Less Take Difference Change From Fewer Reduce by	Times Multiply Groups of Lots of Product Double Square Cube Area Volume	Divide Share among Share equally Fractions of Equal groups Quotient

Once you have recognised what operation the question is asking you to do, it is then important that you select the most appropriate technique so that you can be accurate and also save time. Do not rely on mental arithmetic as this can often lead to mistakes.

In this lesson we will look at both addition and subtraction.

LEARN

Let's look at addition first where you add numbers together. The column technique is probably the most effective and quickest method to use.

Example one: Simple addition
What is 2389 and 467 added together?

Step 1: Put the larger number on top.

Step 2: Keep the digits in their appropriate place value column

Step 3: Don't forget to regroup.

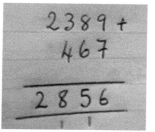

Example two: Addition with a decimal point
What is 928.460 added to 37.923?

Follow steps 1 to 3 above.

Step 4: If you have been asked to add decimals, don't forget to line up the decimal points.

Regrouping is often used in subtraction and addition. It is also known as 'carrying' and 'borrowing' numbers.

LEARN

In subtraction, the column technique will also be the most appropriate for saving time.

Remember to read the question very carefully in order to be able to work out which number needs to be subtracted. If you don't have enough value in the units column you must **exchange** (borrow) and **regroup.**

Example three: Simple subtraction

What is the difference between 605 and 428?

This is where you can exchange and regroup. This is how you can do it:

In the units column 5 is less than 8 so you will need to exchange with the column next to it before starting the subtraction. Since there are no tens you must borrow 10 tens from the hundreds column. Next you must take 1 from the tens column, leaving 9 tens and place it in the units column to give you 15

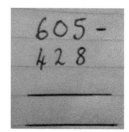

Now you are ready to do the subtraction.

The final answer is 177. You can check whether this is the correct answer using the inverse, by adding 177 to 428. When added together they should make 605

Please be careful. Many questions are written and designed to be confusing and awkward in their wording. Please take a few seconds to recognise the vocabulary and understand what the question is actually asking you to do.

DEVELOP

Try these addition and subtraction questions.

1)   What is 95.6 more than 257.52? = 352·12

2)   Decrease 58.6 by 39.71 = 18·89

3)   Find the sum of 259.6 and 867.83 = 608·23

4)   Take 78.95 from 100.28 = 21·33

5)   Increase 987.4 by 25.6 = 961·8

6)   Take 0.8 from 80 = 79·2

7)   Find the difference between 0.007 and 7 = 6·993

8)   What is the sum of 2098.91 and 879.092? = 1088·008

9)   What change from £1000 do I get if I spend £263.45? = 736·515

10)   Add 9.85, 98.5 and 985 together = 1093·35

Please take care when placing your decimal point back into your answer.

TIMED TEST   15 MINS

1) In one football season at school the Year 5 children score a total of 142 goals and the Year 6 children score a total of 168. How many goals are scored altogether?

A	B	C	D	E
300	301	310	320	315

2) A swimming pool contains 6000 litres of water. If 3214 litres are pumped out to lower the water level, how many litres are left?

A	B	C	D	E
2678L	2786L	2876L	2688L	3686L

3) Claire has a vegetable garden. It is 9.75m long. She increases the length by 2.8m. How long is Claire's garden now?

A	B	C	D	E
12.55m	15.25m	15.15m	18.25m	12.25m

4) Sam puts four lengths of wood together. One is 87.91cm, one is 36.32cm, one is 209.40cm and one is 8.06cm. What is the total sum of their lengths?

A	B	C	D	E
346.19cm	463.19cm	431.69cm	369.46cm	341.69cm

5) Emma is 115cm tall. On Monday she cycles 4 km. On Wednesday she cycles 1.25km less than on the Monday. How many metres does Emma cycle on Wednesday?

A	B	C	D	E
2057m	2570m	5250m	2750m	5270m

6) At the Maths Club Jovan was asked to find the difference in length between two pieces of rope. One was a length of 0.089m and the other was 8.9m. What was the length he calculated?

A	B	C	D	E
8.811m	8.181m	8.118m	1.881m	8.188m

7) Felicity runs the London marathon which is 42.2km long. She runs for 31.5km and she walks for 6.9km before her final run to the finish. How long in km is Felicity's final run?

A	B	C	D	E
4.2km	3.8km	8.3km	3.2km	8.4km

8) My teacher, Mr Dolamore, went on a diet. In month one, he lost 2.5kg, in month two he lost 1.75kg and in month three he lost 2.25kg. In month four he decided to treat himself and eat lots of chocolate and gained 0.66kg. How much weight did Mr Dolamore lose altogether?

A	B	C	D	E
4.85kg	8.54kg	5.48kg	5.49kg	5.84kg

9) The maximum weight allowed in the school lift is 350kg. Four teachers are in the lift, weighing 62.5kg, 60.32kg, 80kg and 83.3kg. If one more person wants to get in the lift, what is the maximum weight they can be?

A	B	C	D	E
88.66kg	86.86kg	66.88kg	68.86kg	63.88kg

10) Pinak runs 7.7km on Monday, 12.3km on Tuesday and 9.5km on Wednesday. How far does Pinak run altogether?

A	B	C	D	E
30.5km	25.9km	28.6km	29.5km	29.05km

11) Paris is a member of various clubs during the week. In addition to her one hour of maths club on a Friday, on a Monday she goes to gym for one and a half hours, on a Tuesday she attends ice skating for one and three quarter hours and on Thursday she is at athletics club for three and a quarter hours. What is the total number of hours that Paris will spend at a club in a week?

A	B	C	D	E
6.5h	5.7h	7.5h	7.25h	5.5h

12) Hafsah was asked in her mental maths test to calculate taking a hundred metres from ten thousand metres. She answered it correctly. What was her answer?

A	B	C	D	E
9000m	9900m	8900m	9190m	9090m

13) Billy had to select 38 photographs from his collection of 201 for an exhibition in his village art festival. How many photographs did he have left?

A	B	C	D	E
153	167	163	165	162

14) The class was asked how many edges there are in three pentagons, two rectangles, two scalene triangles, three isosceles triangles and seven octagons. Help the class find the answer.

A	B	C	D	E
84	89	91	94	86

15) Neil had to deliver Easter eggs to friends and family. He monitored the distance for each journey. His first trip was 12.4 miles, the second trip was 43.9 miles, the third was 0.6 miles, the fourth was 28.8 miles and the final trip was 19.7 miles. How much distance in miles did Neil travel in total?

A	B	C	D	E
150.4	105.4	140.5	104.5	154.5

LEARN

To assist you in multiplication it is important that you know your **times tables**. You should also **estimate** the answers before applying a method to help decide what your answer should roughly look like. This lesson will provide methods to help you solve complex multiplication questions.

Example one: A decimal number multiplied by an integer

6.4×3

You can estimate this by calculating $6 \times 3 = 18$

You know it will be more than 18 as 6.4 is bigger than 6. The actual answer is 19.2

Once you have estimated your answer you can then start your calculation. The formal multiplication technique will be used.

First calculate it without the decimal point.

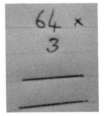 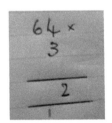 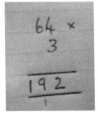

Coding 1: The order of multiplication is:

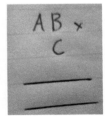 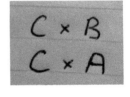

Its important to follow the right order when multiplying to get the correct answer.

LEARN

Once you have the digits in place then you have to accurately place the decimal point into the answer.
Here is a system to help you:

KEY   _____   = digit
            .   = decimal point

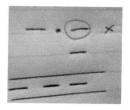 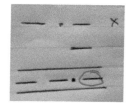 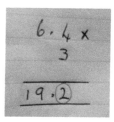

Step 1:
Add in the decimal point from the question and see how many digits are to the right of it. In this example there is only one.

Step 2:
In the answer circle one digit from the right, and place the decimal point to the left of it.

The answer is 19.2

Example two: Two decimal numbers multiplied together

8.2 × 4.9

You can estimate this by calculating 8 × 5 = 40. The actual answer is 40.18

By referring to Coding 1 you can expand it and use Coding 2 to help you with the order of multiplication:

Coding 2

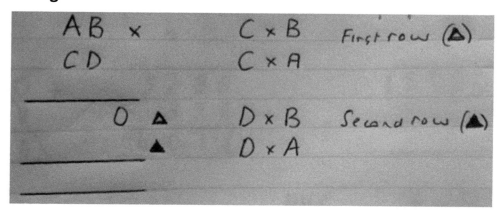

LEARN

Step 1: It is important that you place a zero into the calculation to represent a ten, to indicate that you are multiplying by the 'ten' digit.

Step 2: Along the same line as the zero you multiply everything by 4 (or 40).

Step 3: Then multiply all the digits by 9 in the same order and place the products in the row below.

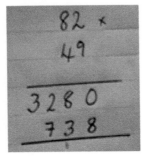

Step 4: Once the multiplication is complete you have to add up the two rows.

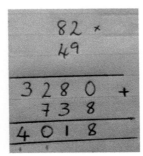

Step 5: You now have to accurately place the decimal point.
Once the decimal point has been added in the calculation you will see here are two digits to the right of it so there will be two digits to the right of a decimal point in the answer.

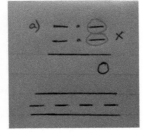

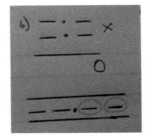

LEARN

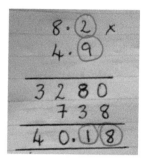

Therefore, your answer is 40.18

Example three: Two-digit number multiplied by a three-digit number
215 × 75
You can estimate this by calculating 200 × 80 = 16000. The actual answer is 16125
Follow the steps taken in Example two.

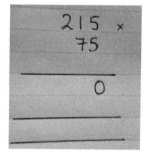

By referring to Coding 2 and expanding it you can use Coding 3 to help you with the order of multiplication:

Coding 3

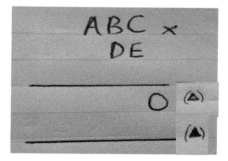

The order of multiplication is:

LEARN

You can now calculate Example 3 by following the Coding 3 order.

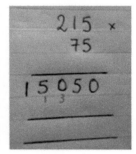

$7 \times 5 = 35$
$7 \times 1 = 7$
$7 \times 2 = 14$

$5 \times 5 = 25$
$5 \times 1 = 5$
$5 \times 2 = 10$

Then add up what has been calculated:

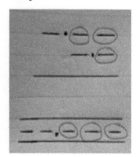

So the answer to 215 × 75 = 16125

If the question has a decimal, as in the example below, you can calculate the answer using the same steps:

Step 1: Circle the digits to the right of the decimal point.

Step 2: As there are three digits to the right of the decimal point, there will be three digits to the right in the answer. Your answer is 16.125 (your estimate was 16).

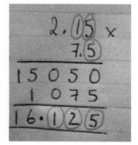

DEVELOP

Try these multiplication questions.

1)   Multiply 20 by 30 = *600*

2)   Find the product of 300 and 90 = *27000*

3)   6 lots of 0.8 = *4·8*

4)   0.4mm times 0.6mm =

5)   Double 28.4 =

6)   Multiply 8 and 865.4 =

7)   Find the product of 28.64 and 3.2 =

8)   Times together 8.3 and 6.7 =

9)   34 lots of £19.75 =

10)   What is the total of 89 groups of 2.68? =

Place the zero in automatically so you don't forget it or your answer will be incorrect.

TIMED TEST　　　　　　　　　**15 MINS**

1) There are 324 beech trees in a forest. There are six times as many oak trees. How many oak trees are there?

A	B	C	D	E
54	9141	972	1944	1494

2) The drama class performed their play 14 times. The average audience for each show was 286. How many people watched their performance altogether?

A	B	C	D	E
4004	4404	4440	300	3000

3) Alice buys 86 special stamps for her collection. Each costs £4.75. How much does Alice pay altogether?

A	B	C	D	E
£405.80	£408.50	£458.50	£485.50	£548.50

4) Myra asks John to build a book shelf for 32 photo albums. Each album is 46.5mm wide. If all the albums were stacked tightly together, what is the minimum width of shelf, in millimetres, that John would need to build?

A	B	C	D	E
1884mm	8184mm	4818mm	1848mm	1488mm

5) The boat carries a total of 23 passengers on each trip from Brightlingsea to Mersea Island. It can do a maximum of 146 trips a day in July. What is the maximum number of passengers it could carry in one day in July?

A	B	C	D	E
3358	3538	3853	3385	3583

6) The school cook orders 324 packets of napkins. There are 45 napkins in each packet. How many individual napkins are ordered altogether?

A	B	C	D	E
15480	15850	14580	14850	18450

7) The school continued to increase its stock of resources. It ordered another 64 new and exciting maths books. There are 326 pages in each book. How many pages are there altogther?

A	B	C	D	E
20488	20468	20846	20864	20684

8) Ben was celebrating the end of his final exams at school by going on holiday with his two best friends. He was going for 18 nights staying at a bed and breakfast for £21.50 a night per person. On the final day of their stay, what was the total bill for Ben and his friends?

A	B	C	D	E
£1261	£1611	£1161	£1160	£1116

9) Jasveer has a total of 32 pets. On average, it costs £0.67 per pet, per day, to feed. What is the total cost in August, to feed his pets?

A	B	C	D	E
£992.87	£664.64	£644.66	£666.44	£99.20

10) It was Naomi's final essay to write for her biology course for the year. The average number of words per line on a page, was 19 and there were 34 lines on a page. She wrote 8 pages in total. What was the total number of words written in her essay?

A	B	C	D	E
5618	5861	5668	6581	5168

11) Paula was preparing for Christmas and decided to knit a set of nativity characters. For each wise man she knitted, on average, 43 stitches per row and 216 rows. She knitted three wise men. How many stitches altogether did she knit?

A	B	C	D	E
26864	26487	27864	27648	27468

12) Brian was asked to be school captain for his football team. He prepared his team for the tournament where six teams in total competed. Each team played each other in the first round, then the two teams with the most points would play in the final. If each game of football lasted 6 minutes each half, how many minutes of football would Brian's eventual winning team have played?

A	B	C	D	E
72	84	42	96	48

13) To celebrate the Queen's 90th birthday, 253 coaches were travelling into London from the South West of England for the weekend. On average, each coach could transport 84 passengers. What was the total number of passengers transported?

A	B	C	D	E
22251	25221	22251	21252	22512

14) It costs Finlay an average of £1.09 per litre of petrol. He would require 42 litres to fill his car tank in one visit to the garage. To travel a return trip to Bristol he needs to fill his tank three times. How much, in pounds, does it cost Finlay to drive the complete trip?

A	B	C	D	E
£137.34	£45.78	£126.00	£91.56	£134.73

15) Olivia becomes a school prefect. She has been given the responsibility to calculate the price of an order. She has to order enough pens for the school for the following term. She needs to buy five boxes per year group. There are six year groups and 50 packets in a box. Each packet costs £5.50. What is Olivia's calculation of the total order price?

A	B	C	D	E
£8520	£8250	£8205	£1650	£1500

LEARN

Division is the **inverse** of multiplication and therefore it is important to know your times tables and to estimate when answering.

For example: 84 divided by 42

You know that 80 divided by 40 is 2 (8 divided by 4 is 2).

Throughout this division section you will be doing the **short division technique**. This is often known as the 'bus stop' method. The chunking method can be used but normally it is a far slower technique.

Example one: Dividing into a three-digit number

726 ÷ 3

In order for you to answer this you will need to take the following steps.

Step 1: Lay the calculation out into the 'bus shelter'.

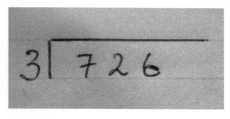

Step 2: How many 3s go into the first digit which is 7 (although you know it is in fact 700)? The answer is 2 with a remainder of 1

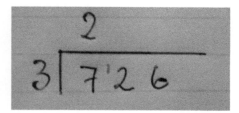

Step 3: How many 3s go into 12? The answer is 4

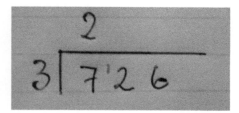

LEARN

Step 4: How many 3s go into 6? The answer is 2

$$3 \overline{)7^{\,}2\,6} = 242$$

The answer to 726 divided by 3 is 242

Example two: Dividing into a five-digit number

What is the quotient of 15618 and 6?

Follow the above steps by working along the 'bus shelter' layout.

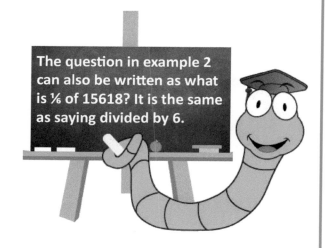

The question in example 2 can also be written as what is ⅙ of 15618? It is the same as saying divided by 6.

The answer to the quotient of 15618 and 6 is 2603

LEARN

Example three: Division and fractions

What is ⅚ of 15618?

First you divide by the denominator (bottom number) which is 6. Then you times the quotient by the numerator (top number).

$$0\,2\,6\,0\,3 \times 5 = 13\,0\,1\,5$$
$$6\,\overline{|\,1\,5^3\,6\,1\,8}$$

Example four: Long division technique

What is 4389 divided by 19?

As you are asked to divide by a number which is more than one digit (19) you will be doing the long division technique. Calculate as if you are using the short division technique but work out the remainders below the bus shelter, forming a 'long shape' calculation.

This is shown below:

a) $19\,\overline{|\,4\,3\,8\,9}$

b) $19\,\overline{|\,4\,3\,8\,9}$ with 0 above

c)
$$
\begin{array}{r}
0\,2 \\
19\,\overline{|\,4\,3\,8\,9} \\
3\,8\downarrow \\
\hline
0\,5\,8
\end{array}
$$

d)
$$
\begin{array}{r}
0\,2\,3\,1 \\
19\,\overline{|\,4\,3\,8\,9} \\
3\,8\downarrow \\
\hline
0\,5\,8 \\
5\,7\downarrow \\
\hline
0\,1\,9 \\
1\,9 \\
\hline
0\,0
\end{array}
$$

$$= 2\,3\,1$$

4389 divided by 19 = 231

DEVELOP

Have a go at the following questions.

1) Divide 175 by 5 =

2) What is ½ of 5678? =

3) What is ⅗ of 51025? =

4) What is the quotient of 82104 and 24? =

5) Share 5544 among 24 =

6) How many 30s go into 4260? =

7) What is 3744 divided by 16? =

8) What is the quotient of 15408 and 48? =

9) What is ⅔ of 720? =

10) Divide 11802 by 21 =

TIMED TEST   15 MINS

1) Jessica buys eight pencils for 96p. What is the cost of one pencil?
    A   B   C   D   E
    15p   12p   £7.68   16p   13p

2) Sophia spends £6 on 24 large oranges. What is the cost of one orange?
    A   B   C   D   E
    £0.24   £1.44   £2.50   £0.25   £0.40

3) The school canteen makes 540 ham rolls every day. One packet of ham makes 15
    rolls. How many packets of ham does the canteen need to purchase for each day?
    A   B   C   D   E
    8100   32   360   320   36

4) A class competition has been introduced to Miriam's year group at school. It is to
    collect as many merit marks as possible. A special award will be given to each
    person gaining 400 merit marks. Miriam estimates she can get 16 merit marks a
    week. How many weeks will it take Miriam to get 400 merit marks?
    A   B   C   D   E
    64   46   52   25   40

5) Peter is working at an international school in the summer holiday. He is asked to
    organise a school trip for 255 students. 17 teachers accompany them. All
    the teachers have the same number of students in their groups. How many
    students are in each group?
    A   B   C   D   E
    17   25   18   14   15

6) A ream of paper contains 500 sheets. For Louise's geography project she shares
    out one ream equally among 24 students. How many complete sheets does each
    student have?
    A   B   C   D   E
    20   15   18   21   28

7) Naomi bought a packet of 12 doughnuts for £3. What is the price of one
    doughnut?
    A   B   C   D   E
    36p   30p   24p   21p   25p

8) Myra has asked John to sort out his garden shed. John collects a total of 578 loose nails. He purchases 17 small containers and fills each with the same number of nails. How many nails can each container hold?

A	B	C	D	E
36	41	33	34	43

9) Vijay has been asked in a maths challenge question to calculate the third dimension of a box with a volume of 120 cubic metres. He has been given two of the dimensions already. The area of one face is 24 metres squared. What is Vijay's correct calculation for the length of the box?

A	B	C	D	E
8m	2m	4m	3m	5m

10) A theatre is filled with drama students from 25 schools. Each coach transports the same number of student passengers from each school. There are 700 seats available for the students. How many students does each coach transport?

A	B	C	D	E
23	175	25	28	82

11) Miriam was collecting up a range of toys for her babysitting job. She had various bags containing separate shapes. She decided to take her square based pyramid bag. In total the bag contained 60 vertices. How many square based pyramids did Miriam take?

A	B	C	D	E
15	12	10	18	13

12) At a summer camp a total of 3 meals a day will be provided for each child. On average there will be 285 meals provided each day. How many children will attend, on average, each day?

A	B	C	D	E
75	78	85	95	97

13) A half-hour study at an airport calculated the total flight distance travelled by 42 planes. It measured 98322 kilometres. What was the average distance travelled by each plane?

A	B	C	D	E
2341km	3241km	4321km	1432km	2431km

14) Megan was working at a sheep farm over the summer. It was made up of 1920 sheep. She had to work out $\frac{8}{30}$ of the flock that were to be sold on to another farm. How many sheep did she calculate?

A	B	C	D	E
64	84	640	512	240

15) Richard and Michael go on a fishing trip together over 3 days. Richard catches a total of 33 fish and Michael a total of 51 fish. How many fish, on average, do they each catch per day?

A	B	C	D	E
28	42	14	24	41

LEARN

Multiplying by 10, 100 and 1000

When multiplying by the **powers of 10** it is important to start at the decimal point. Look back to Lesson 1 to help you understand the value of different digits.

As you know, the position of the decimal point is 'fixed' (a bit like a drawing pin fixed to the wall) but there is a technique to help you. You may wish to consider this for the purpose of working out only.

When a number is multiplied, the value gets bigger.

If you multiply a number by **10** the digits move to the left one place and grow, in value, ten times (or you can say the decimal point looks as if it moves or 'jumps' to the right one place as there is one zero in 10).

If you multiply by **100** the digits move to the left two places and grow, in value, a hundred times (or you can say the decimal point looks as if it moves, or 'jumps' to the right two places, as there are two zeros in 100).

If you multiply by **1000** the digits move to the left three places and grow, in value, a thousand times (or you can say the decimal point looks as if it moves, or 'jumps' to the right three places as there are three zeros in 1000).

This process of multiplying by the powers of 10 is illustrated below:

Example one: Simple multiplication with powers of 10, 100 and 1000

$4 \times 10 = 40$

$4 \times 100 = 400$

$4 \times 1000 = 4000$

LEARN

Example two: Powers of 10 multiplication with a decimal point

2.4 × 10 = 24
2.4 × 100 = 240
2.4 × 1000 = 2400

More examples:

31.64 × 10 = 316.4
0.71 × 100 = 71
0.82 × 1000 = 820

The word multiplication starts with **m** and you move or jump the decimal point to the right.

Dividing by 10, 100 and 1000

As division is the inverse of multiplication, the process uses the same principle but takes the 'opposite direction'. Therefore you move the numbers to the right, or 'jump' the decimal point to the left.

Example three: Simple division with powers of 10, 100 and 1000

4 ÷ 10 = 0.4
4 ÷ 100 = 0.04
4 ÷ 1000 = 0.004

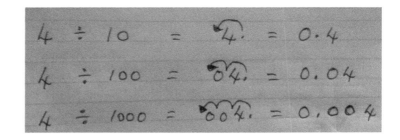

More examples:

13.9 ÷ 10 = 1.39
13.9 ÷ 100 = 0.139
13.9 ÷ 1000 = 0.0139

7. DEVELOP

Try the following questions.

1)   7.34 × 10 =

2)   89.2 × 100 =

3)   0.03 × 1000 =

4)   8 ÷ 10 =

5)   65.7 ÷ 100 =

6)   5 ÷ 1000 =

7)   678 ÷ 100 =

8)   7.4 ÷ 1000 =

9)   2.1 × 1000 =

10)   0.8 × 1000 =

The decimal point is very powerful and its position determines the value of the number. You must therefore make it very clear. If the decimal point has no digit to the left, put a '0' (or 'Bodyguard') to the left of the decimal, to help 'protect' the decimal point.
For example, .34 now becomes 0.34

LEARN

If you are given a calculation with a mixture of operations, it is important to follow a rule. This rule ensures that **you do the operations in a certain order**. If the operations are not carried out in the correct order, then the answer will be wrong.

BIDMAS gives you the order in which operations should be carried out.
Remember BIDMAS stands for:

Brackets: if there are brackets, work out the value of the expression inside the brackets
Indices: this includes powers, such as square or cube numbers or square roots or cube roots
Divide: if there are no brackets or indices, do the division next
Multiplication: this follows next in order of operation no matter where it is in the expression
Add: if the expression has only these operations in, then work it out from left to right
Subtract: this would be the last operation to perform

Example one:

$3 + (6 \div 3) - 1$
$= 3 + 2 - 1$
$= 5 - 1$
$= 4$

Example two:

$3 + 2 \times 5 - 1$
$= 3 + 10 - 1$
$= 13 - 1$
$= 12$

Example three:

$(8 + 2)^2 - 4 \times 3^2$
$= 10^2 - 4 \times 9$
$= 100 - 36$
$= 64$

BIDMAS is a bit like baking a cake. You need to know what order to add the ingredients.

DEVELOP

Use BIDMAS to answer the following questions.

1) $3 \times 4^2 =$

2) $30 \div (4 \div 2) + 3 =$

3) $20 \div 2^2 =$

4) $7 + 24 \div 6 =$

5) $(16 \div 8)^2 + 2 \times 3 =$

6) $3 \times (5^2 - 4^2) =$

7) $40 \div (12 - 4) =$

8) $(3 + 9) \div (3 + 1) =$

9) $2 + (2^3 \times 1) \times 4 =$

10) $2^2 \times (3 + 1^2)^3 =$

Other BIDMAS questions you could get are:
Make the expressions correct by replacing the * with + − × or ÷ and use brackets if required.

Example 1:   3 * 7 * 2 = 20 becomes $3 + 7 \times 2$
Example 2:   5 * 8 * 2 * 4 * 3 = 6 becomes $5 + (8 \times 2) \div 4 - 3$

Try:

i)   4 * 2 * 8 = 10

ii)   5 * 4 * 6 * 8 = 21

iii)   2 * 6 * 3 * 4 = 10

iv)   1 * 3 * 8 * 6 * 2 = 3

TIMED TEST   15 MINS

1) Sarah's cake recipe requires 14 eggs. She is making a surprise cake for her mum's 50th birthday and needs to cater for a lot of guests. Sarah calculates she needs to make the cake 8 times bigger than the one in the recipe. If each egg costs 21p, how much will she need to spend in total on the eggs?

A	B	C	D	E
£20.94	£2.94	£23.52	£1.68	£16.84

2) Gareth takes 15 seconds to swim one length of the pool. If he swims for 5 minutes, how many lengths did he swim?

A	B	C	D	E
20	22	18	75	70

3) Anne was buying presents for her friends. She spent £24 on her best friend and half the amount on eight of her other friends. What is the maximum amount of £20 notes she could have used?

A	B	C	D	E
24	8	120	12	6

4) Molly, the dog, had a birthday party. Eleven other dogs attended her party. All the dogs were healthy. If there are five claws per paw, how many claws were there altogether at the party?

A	B	C	D	E
160	240	20	60	120

5) The Planets is a piece of music composed by Gustav Holst. It is divided into seven sections, each named after a planet. The section called 'Mars' is 6 minutes and 7 seconds in length and the section called 'Venus' is 8 minutes and 23 seconds in length. What is the difference in length, in seconds, between the two sections?

A	B	C	D	E
306 secs	503 secs	367 secs	136 secs	186 secs

6) A small bottle of oil contains 300ml, a medium bottle contains 750ml and a large bottle contains 1.5 litres. How many litres of oil do the three bottles contain altogether?

A	B	C	D	E
25L	3.75L	255L	15.75L	2.55L

7) Oliver earns a total of £8.50 an hour for doing babysitting for his two sisters. He babysits for three hours a night for two evenings every week, for two years. On his final night he is given a £50 tip for all his fantastic work. How much does he earn altogether?

A	B	C	D	E
£5354	£5304	£1326	£6231	£75.50

8) Trevor is preparing his vegetable garden and plants cabbage out neatly in six rows. In each row there are 26 cabbages. He also plants lettuce in eight rows, with 18 in each row. He decides to dig two more rows and plants 32 cauliflowers in total. How many vegetables altogether has he planted out?

A	B	C	D	E
364	330	332	188	176

9) Myra uses eight pineapples to make 600 ml of pineapple juice. How many pineapples would Myra need to use to make enough juice to fill eight 750 ml bottles?

A	B	C	D	E
80	24	93	10	40

10) There are 60 cows in a herd. Alice has been asked to milk the cows for three days in the school holidays. The total amount of milk produced by the herd in one day is 2280 litres. Over the three days how many litres of milk did each cow produce?

A	B	C	D	E
141L	180L	760L	38L	114L

11) Hannah was raising money to go on a three-week school trip to South Africa. She decided to sell a range of toys. She had bought twenty-eight of the toys for £1.25 each and all sold for £1.75 each. What was the total profit made from those particular toys?

A	B	C	D	E
£49	£14	£84	£78	£35

12) Last Wednesday $\frac{3}{8}$ of the pupils at Hafsah's school were absent. There are 560 children altogether at the school. How many pupils attended school that day?

A	B	C	D	E
70	140	350	210	280

13) Four supermarkets each order 36 crates of jam. Each crate holds 180 jars. How many jars altogether, have the supermarkets ordered?

A	B	C	D	E
6480	25920	12960	720	24860

14) Nishaan has 284 football cards. He puts them all in a scrap book which contains 24 pages. Each page holds 12 cards. He fills all the pages except the last page. How many cards does Nishaan stick into the last page?

A	B	C	D	E
8	12	10	11	7

15) Ben has started his driving lessons. Each lesson costs £26. He has been given £85 for Christmas towards the lessons and £117 for his birthday towards the lessons. He aims to do a maximum of 12 lessons. How much more money has Ben got to save to afford the lessons?

A	B	C	D	E
£312	£202	£140	£110	£250

SECTION 2:
EQUIVALENT NUMBERS

Often when you first learn the basic fractions it can be easier to visualise them in a **fraction wall**. The image below can help you understand equivalent values. For example, how many eighths are in one quarter? The wall clearly shows ⅜ is the same as ¼.

1 whole											
$\frac{1}{2}$						$\frac{1}{2}$					
$\frac{1}{3}$				$\frac{1}{3}$				$\frac{1}{3}$			
$\frac{1}{4}$			$\frac{1}{4}$			$\frac{1}{4}$			$\frac{1}{4}$		
$\frac{1}{5}$		$\frac{1}{5}$		$\frac{1}{5}$		$\frac{1}{5}$		$\frac{1}{5}$			
$\frac{1}{6}$		$\frac{1}{6}$		$\frac{1}{6}$		$\frac{1}{6}$		$\frac{1}{6}$		$\frac{1}{6}$	
$\frac{1}{8}$	$\frac{1}{8}$	$\frac{1}{8}$	$\frac{1}{8}$	$\frac{1}{8}$	$\frac{1}{8}$	$\frac{1}{8}$	$\frac{1}{8}$				
$\frac{1}{10}$	$\frac{1}{10}$	$\frac{1}{10}$	$\frac{1}{10}$	$\frac{1}{10}$	$\frac{1}{10}$	$\frac{1}{10}$	$\frac{1}{10}$	$\frac{1}{10}$	$\frac{1}{10}$		
$\frac{1}{12}$	$\frac{1}{12}$	$\frac{1}{12}$	$\frac{1}{12}$	$\frac{1}{12}$	$\frac{1}{12}$	$\frac{1}{12}$	$\frac{1}{12}$	$\frac{1}{12}$	$\frac{1}{12}$	$\frac{1}{12}$	$\frac{1}{12}$

In this lesson you will be focusing on finding **fractions** of quantities and applying your knowledge of fractions to word problems. Firstly, you need to learn the correct terminology when solving fraction questions. The bottom number is called the 'denominator' and indicates how many parts you have altogether, while the top number is referred to as the 'numerator' as it indicates how many parts of the whole you have.

$$2/3 = \frac{2}{3}$$

numerator

denominator

To find a fraction of a quantity you need to divide the amount by the denominator and multiply by the numerator. You must always simplify the fraction to its lowest term.

Here is an example:
In a school car park there were 56 cars. ⅜ of them were red in colour. How many red cars were in the school car park?

$56 \div 8 = 7$ $7 \times 3 = 21$ 21 cars were red

DEVELOP

Find the fractions of the following quantities.

1) $\frac{6}{7}$ of 42 =

2) $\frac{4}{9}$ of 81 =

3) $\frac{8}{11}$ of 121 =

4) $\frac{5}{12}$ of 144 =

5) $\frac{7}{13}$ of 78 =

6) $\frac{9}{17}$ of 51 =

7) $\frac{12}{24}$ of 240 =

8) $\frac{4}{6}$ of 1200 =

9) $\frac{19}{25}$ of 3000 =

10) $\frac{27}{50}$ of 4000 =

Remember to divide the quantity by the denominator (bottom number) and multiply by the numerator (top number).

TIMED TEST   15 MINS

1) A golfer hit 100 balls at the golf range. He hit $\frac{5}{25}$ of the balls over 250 yards. How many balls did he not hit that far?

A	B	C	D	E
60	40	20	80	30

2) If $\frac{6}{7}$ of Lily's pocket money is £4.20, how much does she have in total?

A	B	C	D	E
£4.80	£4.50	£5.00	£4.40	£4.90

3) Jack's house is 600m from Grange school. He walks to and from school every day. What fraction of 3km does he walk in one day?

A	B	C	D	E
$\frac{2}{5}$	$\frac{3}{5}$	$\frac{1}{5}$	$\frac{3}{6}$	$\frac{4}{5}$

4) A baby slept for 8 hours every night. If the total number of sleeping hours was 56 in a week, what fraction of hours did the baby sleep on Tuesday and Wednesday?

A	B	C	D	E
$\frac{4}{7}$	$\frac{3}{7}$	$\frac{3}{8}$	$\frac{2}{7}$	$\frac{5}{8}$

5) An athlete drank 5 litres of water while at the World Championships. Each bottle holds 250ml. What fraction in the simplest form of the total is four bottles?

A	B	C	D	E
$\frac{6}{20}$	$\frac{1}{10}$	$\frac{5}{20}$	$\frac{1}{5}$	$\frac{2}{10}$

6) On Bracken Farm there were 51 sheep, 20 cows, 19 ducks and 5 horses. What fraction of the animals were ducks?

A	B	C	D	E
$\frac{1}{4}$	$\frac{1}{5}$	$\frac{1}{6}$	$\frac{2}{5}$	$\frac{4}{6}$

7) Nigel spends 3 hours on the train every week day. What fraction of the day does Nigel spend on the train?

A	B	C	D	E
$\frac{1}{4}$	$\frac{1}{8}$	$\frac{4}{24}$	$\frac{3}{12}$	$\frac{5}{6}$

8) How many thirds are there in $6\frac{2}{3}$?

A	B	C	D	E
18	20	30	22	24

9) Brian has ¾ kg of liquorice allsorts. If he gives ⅛ to Alex, what fraction will he have left?

A	B	C	D	E
⅝	⁴⁄₈	⅛	²⁄₈	⅜

10) Jason spends ⅓ of his pocket money on clothes and ⅖ on stationery for school. If he had £45 to spend, how much money does Jason have left?

A	B	C	D	E
£24	£18	£12	£15	£40

11) A car journey is 120 miles. Anita has driven ⅗ of the journey before she needs to get fuel. How many miles are left in the journey?

A	B	C	D	E
40 miles	24 miles	72 miles	12 miles	48 miles

12) A farmer owns 480 hectares of land. He plants swedes on ⁴⁄₁₆ of his land. On the rest of the farm he grows wheat. How many hectares does he use for wheat?

A	B	C	D	E
320h	340h	360h	120h	300h

13) An engineer tests 900 components on a new aircraft. On day 1 she checks ³⁄₁₂ of the parts and on the following day ²⁄₁₂. How many parts does the engineer have left to test?

A	B	C	D	E
525	400	375	300	3000

14) Louise places an advert in a local magazine. The cost of the advert is £20 for each ⅛ of a page. An advert uses ⁶⁄₁₆ of a page. How much does the advert cost?

A	B	C	D	E
£50	£60	£80	£30	£70

15) In a recent survey, 500 people were asked how they would vote in the next election. These were the results:

    220 Conservative
    200 Labour
    80 Other

What fraction of the total would vote 'other'?

A	B	C	D	E
⅕	¼	⁴⁄₂₅	⅙	⁶⁄₂₅

LEARN

Decimals are numbers that are between two whole numbers. For example, 4.2 is between the number 4 and 5. It is 'more than' 4 but 'less than' 5. You can use the knowledge gained in Lesson 1 to help you in this section.

Let's look at a decimal number:

6.75

- The number to the left of the decimal point is a whole integer.
- The numbers to the right of the decimal point are parts of the whole numbers.

When comparing decimal numbers it is important to make sure the **decimal points** line up. Let's compare 5.671 and 5.617 to see which number is the largest. Take a look at the table below. Both the units and the tenths column have the same digits so you need to look at the hundredths column: 5.671 is larger as it has seven hundredths whereas 5.617 only has one hundredth. In this example there is no need to compare the thousandths column.

units	decimal point	tenths	hundredths	thousandths
5	.	6	7	1
5	.	6	1	7

It is important that you can add, subtract, multiply and divide decimal numbers in 11+ maths. When adding or subtracting you can use the same methods that you learnt in the earlier lessons.

Remember to always keep the decimal point in the same column when adding and subtracting decimal numbers.

DEVELOP

Have a go at these decimal questions.

1) Calculate 3.24 + 2.67 =

2) Add together 6.95 and 7.67 =

3) What is the difference between 8.94 and 7.5?

4) By how much is 9.8 greater than 0.7?

5) Subtract 19.43 and 12.98 from 40 =

6) What is 18 ÷ 0.9?

7) Find 0.7 × 1.5 =

8) Total 123.56, 10.23 and 2.09 =

9) What is the product of 4.5 and 4.5?

10) Calculate 8.65 + 5.43 =

Make sure you understand the value of each digit e.g. tenth, hundredth, thousandth.

TIMED TEST   15 MINS

1)   What is the product of 1.5 × 1.5?
      A   B   C   D   E
      2.35   2.45   3   2.55   2.25

2)   Find the difference between 0.2 and 0.02
      A   B   C   D   E
      0.17   0.16   0.18   0.01   0.04

3)   What must be added to 38.2 to equal 50?
      A   B   C   D   E
      11.7   11.8   11.6   12   11.5

4)   Which decimal number is the median?
      3.03   3.33   3.3   3.42   3.333
      A   B   C   D   E
      3.03   3.33   3.3   3.42   3.333

5)   Calculate 93.41 + 5.6
      A   B   C   D   E
      99.01   99.02   99.03   98.02   98.03

6)   What is 6 ÷ 1.2?
      A   B   C   D   E
      4   3   2   5   6

7)   What is the total of £3.21 + £0.78 + £6.01?
      A   B   C   D   E
      £10   £11   £9   £12   £8

8)   What is the sum of the following amounts?
      1.45m   0.35m   152cm
      A   B   C   D   E
      3.33m   3.32m   15.45m   3.52m   3.34m

9) Three athletes competed in a long jump competition. They jumped 7.70m, 7.99m and 8.01m. What was the average?

A	B	C	D	E
8.0m	8.1m	8.2m	7.8m	7.9m

10) Start at 12.6 and count back 15 tenths. What number do you finish on?

A	B	C	D	E
11.3	11.1	2.4	11.2	12.1

11) Calculate $7 \div 0.5$

A	B	C	D	E
4	14	15	16	17

12) A bottle holds 330ml of tomato juice. How many bottles can be made from 1.7 litres?

A	B	C	D	E
6	4	5	7	8

13) Bella saved some of her pocket money for six weeks.
She saved   88p   £8   80p   £8.08   888p   £0.80
How much did she save altogether?

A	B	C	D	E
£27.43	£27.44	£28.44	£27.40	£28.09

14) Jake had 1.2 litres of orange juice and James had 800ml of apple juice. John drank 100cl of grapefruit juice. How much juice was consumed altogether?

A	B	C	D	E
3L	3.02L	3.04L	3.05L	3.1L

15) Calculate $1.1 \times 1.1 \times 1.1$

A	B	C	D	E
13.33	1.321	1.334	1.331	133.1

LEARN

In this lesson you will be solving percentage problems. It is important to understand that 'per cent' means '**out of 100**'. If you score 85% on a test then, if there were a possible 100 marks altogether, you will achieve 85 marks.

So 85% = $^{85}/_{100}$

Having a secure understanding of your factors of 100 will help you solve many percentage questions. Below are listed the factors of 100.:

2, 4, 5, 10, 20, 25, 50, 100

Therefore, if you think of the factors in pairs, 1 × 100, 2 × 50, 4 × 25, 5 × 20 and 10 × 10, this will help you decipher many different percentage questions.

For example what is 13 out of 20 as a percentage?

Let's imagine you have scored 13 out of 20 in a spelling test at school and we need to record the answer as a percentage. The number 20 has a factor pair of 5 and this can be useful to convert this raw score into a percentage. See the method below:

$$\frac{13}{20} \times \frac{5}{5} = \frac{65}{100} = 65\%$$

It is important to realise that to find 1% of a number you divide by 100 and if you are finding 10% of a number you divide by 10. In the 'Develop' section, see if you can use these key facts to help you.

DEVELOP

Find the following percentages of these amounts.

1)   10% of 80 =

2)   15% of 60 =

3)   20% of 120 =

4)   35% of 200 =

5)   50% of 1500 =

6)   70% of 3000 =

7)   5% of 300 =

8)   6% of 900 =

9)   23% of 150 =

10)   46% of 800 =

A useful tip when trying to find 5% of a number is to find 10% first and then halve the answer.

TIMED TEST   15 MINS

1) In Highpoint School there were 200 children on roll. 2% of the students were absent on one day. How many children were present?

A	B	C	D	E
4	196	190	8	2

2) There were 600 children's books in the local library. 180 of them were non-fiction, the rest were fiction. What percentage were fiction books?

A	B	C	D	E
60%	50%	70%	65%	30%

3) A mahogany table costs £120, but you need to add 20% VAT. What is its real price?

A	B	C	D	E
£96	£140	£132	£144	£100

4) In a science test out of 80 Catherine scored 60. What percentage is this?

A	B	C	D	E
25%	75%	60%	80%	65%

5) In a sale a jacket usually costing £160 is reduced by 25%. What is the new cost of the coat?

A	B	C	D	E
£120	£140	£135	£125	£180

6) If the cost of a garden shed is £300 in September but it will increase by 15% in October, what will the garden shed cost in October?

A	B	C	D	E
£255	£315	£285	£310	£345

7) Henry bought a car for £4200 but, after making some repairs, he sold it for 21% more than he purchased it for. What was the new sale price?

A	B	C	D	E
£4620	£5082	£4242	£4221	£5042

8) A hospital contains 320 beds. If 25% are empty, how many are being used?

A	B	C	D	E
400	260	240	460	230

9) In a cash ISA account you can earn an interest of 4%. How much will be made on £1800?

A	B	C	D	E
£1818	£1872	£1836	£1804	£1796

10) A laptop computer costs £1100. It is reduced by 5% in a sale. What is the sale price of the computer?

A	B	C	D	E
£1035	£1045	£1055	£1020	£1030

11) Barrie decides to invest £3500 in a pension scheme and earn 8% interest. How much interest does he receive?

A	B	C	D	E
£250	£270	£260	£240	£280

12) Susanna's hourly wage rises from £7.20 to £7.92. What percentage increase is this?

A	B	C	D	E
8%	5%	10%	6%	7%

13) A cheese-burger, chips and a drink costs £4.50 but from tomorrow the cost will increase by 10%. What will the cost of the meal change to?

A	B	C	D	E
£4.95	£4.05	£4.55	£4.00	£5.05

14) A colony of 300 Emperor penguins was depleted by 7% due to severe weather. How many Emperor penguins were left in the group?

A	B	C	D	E
270	279	293	260	278

15) The Smith family purchased a house for £250000 five years ago. They sell the property for £450000. What was the percentage increase?

A	B	C	D	E
50%	60%	80%	90%	40%

SECTION 3:
ALGEBRA

LEARN

The **nth term** is a rule, or expression, to describe the number pattern of a sequence. It can be used to find any number (or term) in a number sequence.

You may be given the first five terms of a sequence and then be asked to find the 20th term or 50th term, for example.

The nth term can also be used to identify whether a number is in the sequence.

Example one

n   =   the number in the sequence

n   =   1   2   3   4   ⟶

term =   2   4   6   8

At this level in maths you will be given an nth term expression (or rule). With the above example the nth term is 2n because:

n	=	$1_{\times2}$	$2_{\times2}$	$3_{\times2}$	$4_{\times2}$	$20_{\times2}$	$100_{\times2}$
term	=	2	4	6	8	40	200

You could be asked for the 20th term and the 100th term by using the rule 2n.

Example two

n	=	$1\,n^2$	$2\,n^2$	$3\,n^2$	$4\,n^2$	$30\,n^2$	$50\,n^2$
term	=	1	4	9	16	900	2500

The nth term expression (or rule) here is n^2.

So therefore you could be asked to find the 30th term.

Tip: If you are asked to recognise what expression describes the sequence, it is a good idea to number (n) each term of the sequence 1, 2, 3, etc.

DEVELOP

For questions 1, 2 and 3, look at the sequence and select the expression which could be used to find the nth term.

1)   2,   5,   8,   11,   14

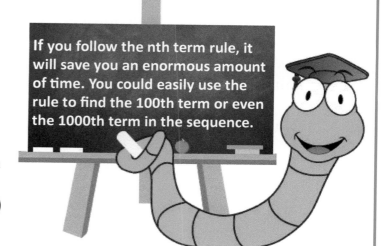

If you follow the nth term rule, it will save you an enormous amount of time. You could easily use the rule to find the 100th term or even the 1000th term in the sequence.

   a) $3n - 4$ c) $n + 1$

   b) n^2 d) $3n - 1$

2)   9,   16,   25,   36,   49

   a) $n \div 2$ c) $(n + 2)^2$

   b) $4n$ d) $(n^2 + 2)$

3) $- 2$,   1,   6,   13,   22

   a) $n - 3$ c) $(2n) - 1$

   b) $(n + 1)^2$ d) $n^2 - 3$

4)   What is the 4th term when using the formula: $n \div 2 + 1$?

5)   Write the 10th term for the expression: $4n - 2 =$

6)   What is the 5th term of the sequence with the nth term rule: $n^2 - 5$?

7)   Write the 100th term for the formula: $2(n - 1) =$

8)   Write the 15th term for the expression: $4n - 3 =$

9)   What is the number in the sequence for the expression: n^2 is 100?

10)   With the expression $6n - 4$, is it correct to say the 3rd term is 14? Yes or no.

LEARN

Algebra is where shapes or letters are used instead of numbers: this is called **algebraic substitution**. Below are some examples of substitutions with shapes or letters as numbers. This is important as it helps to find out about the unknown. You can use algebra in real life problems and use equations to try to solve them.

Example one: Algebraic substitution

1)   3 Δ 4 = 12   Δ = ×

2)   8 ☆ 4 = 2   ☆ = ÷

3)   6 × t = 24   t = 4

4)   21 ÷ a = 7   a = 3

It is important to be able to simplify algebra, especially when the equations become more complicated in order to help work out the answer. Let's look at some examples – it's all about collecting 'like' (same) terms.

Example two: Simplifying expressions

1)   T + T + T = 3T

2)   H + H + W + W = 2H + 2W

3)   3 × n = 3n

4)   8 ÷ J = 8/J

5)   X × Y × Z = XYZ

6)   3 × R + 2 = 3R + 2

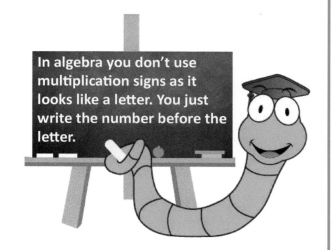

In algebra you don't use multiplication signs as it looks like a letter. You just write the number before the letter.

DEVELOP

Can you work out what numbers the letters represent below?

1) $M \times 8 = 16$ What is M?

2) $28 \div t = 4$ What is t?

3) $5 + w = 14$ What is w?

4) $46 - y = 25$ What is y?

5) $H \div 5 = 9$ What is H?

Algebraic substitution questions could also be in the form of starting with known values of letters. For example, if P = 8 and Q = 9, what is P + Q? The answer is 17

With the values of A, B, C given below, try the following questions.

A = 5   B = 6   C = 10

6) $A + B =$

7) $3B =$

8) $AB \div 3 =$

9) $A + 2B + C =$

10) $BC - A =$

Below are some questions for you to try to simplify.

11) $d + d =$

12) $c \times c \times c =$

13) $14k \div 7 =$

14) $16d \div d =$

15) $12y \div 4y =$

LEARN

Algebraic equations are also known as 'balanced' equations as the value on the left side of the equals sign is the same as on the right.

Example one: 4x = 20

The aim is to solve the equation and find the value of the 'unknown' or letter which in this example is x. The letter needs to be on one side of the equals sign and the numbers on the other.

> A bit like balancing the equation on a set of weighing scales.

$4x = 20$

You need to make the 4 on the left of the equals sign 'magically disappear' and 'reappear' on the right side of the sign. This is done by cancelling out the multiplication. You can cancel out the multiplication of 4 by the inverse operation, division.

$x = 20 \div 4$

$x = 5$

Check whether the answer is correct, $4 \times 5 = 20$

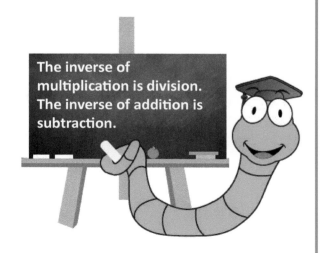

> The inverse of multiplication is division. The inverse of addition is subtraction.

LEARN

Example two: 2p + 3 = 13

What is the value of p? The aim is to get rid of the 'floater' number (+ 3) first. You need to make it magically disappear by 'cancelling' it out. The inverse of +3 is −3

2p + 3 = 13

2p = 13 − 3

2p = 10

Then we need to make the '2' on the left vanish and reappear on the right of the equals sign. 2p means p is multiplied by 2, therefore the inverse would be to divide by 2.

2p = 10

p = 10 ÷ 2

p = 5

Then check whether p is 5 by substituting p with 5. This is 2 x 5 + 3 = 13

Example three: C ÷ 4 − 2 = 1

Get rid of the 'floater' first.

C ÷ 4 − 2 = 1

    +2   +2 ⬅ | Balance out the 'floater' by adding 2 to each side

C ÷ 4 = 1 + 2

C ÷ 4 = 3

  ×4   ×4 ⬅ | Balance further by multiplying each side by 4

C = 3 × 4

C = 12

Check your answer by substituting C with 12:

12 ÷ 4 − 2 = 1

C = 12

LEARN

Example four: Linear equations

In the exam you may get asked to solve a linear equation which is an equation between two variables that give a straight line when plotted on a graph. There are often unknowns on both sides of the equals sign.

Get the letters to one side (on the left) and the numbers on the other (to the right).

$6m - 17 = m + 3$

$6m - m - 17 = 3$

$5m = 3 + 17$

$5m = 20$

$m = 20 \div 5$

$m = 4$

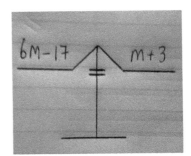

Check your answer using the substitution process:

$(6 \times 4) - 17 = 4 + 3$

$7 = 7$

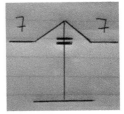

Example five: Applying algebra knowledge to word problems

Audrey had six house points. From her history project she has just been given more house points (H). How many house points (H) was Audrey awarded for history?
The 'unknown' is the number of house points (H) and you can translate the question into a maths algebraic equation:

$6 + H = 10$

$H = 10 - 6$

$\underline{H = 4}$

Answer: Audrey was awarded 4 house points for history.

DEVELOP

Have a go at solving the following algebraic equations.

1) $2y + 5 = 17$ $y =$

2) $5R - 9 = 31$ $R =$

3) $14n - 20 = 22$ $n =$

4) $41 = 7M + 6$ $M =$

5) $9 + 16W = 73$ $W =$

6) $R/8 + 6 = 10$ $R =$

7) $J/7 - 5 = 3$ $J =$

8) $T/24 + 28 = 32$ $T =$

9) $7y - 11 = y + 1$ $y =$

10) $17x - 6 = 9x + 2$ $x =$

TIMED TEST

15 MINS

1) With the expression $n^3 + 1$, what is the 5th term?

A	B	C	D	E
124	116	120	126	130

2) What is the 15th term for the expression $4n - 3$?

A	B	C	D	E
57	63	37	42	48

3) If A = 3, B = 8 and C = 10, what is the answer for (B + C)A?

A	B	C	D	E
40	60	38	45	54

4) What is the answer after simplifying $6 \times e - 2 \times e$?

A	B	C	D	E
8e	7e	4e	4e + 2	6e − 2

5) Simplify $g + g + 2 \times h + g$

A	B	C	D	E
2g + 2h + g	3g 2h	3g × 2h	3g + 2h	2g × 2h + g

6) What does A stand for in the following equation?

$A \div 10 - 5 = 5$

A	B	C	D	E
5	50	100	75	10

7) Sarah plays a game of thinking of a number. She then halves it and takes 16 from it. She is left with 34. What was the number she was thinking of?

A	B	C	D	E
150	100	50	68	32

8) When Kieran got his pocket money, he spent £2.30 on sweets and had £4.20 left. How much pocket money did he get?

A	B	C	D	E
£4.60	£4.30	£4.20	£6.50	£6.20

9) Stacey is preparing for an Easter gathering. She makes 12 hot cross buns and 16 chocolate nests. She eats 2 chocolate nests as she is feeling hungry. She makes gingerbread bunny biscuits and an Easter cake. If she puts 56 different treats on the table, how many bunny biscuits did she make?

A	B	C	D	E
29	56	41	39	51

10) Heather wanted to knit a nativity scene for Christmas. She bought 22 balls of wool in total: 6 were beige, 4 green, 2 brown, 5 purple, 2 yellow and the rest were red. How many balls of wool were red?

A	B	C	D	E
29	19	13	22	3

11) Olly bought 4 football tickets. They each cost £F. He had to pay a booking fee of £7 and four train tickets which each cost £15. His total expense was £195.00. How much was one football ticket?

A	B	C	D	E
£195	£188	£32	£128	£38

12) Ann had a bag of grapes. She ate 6, gave 8 to each of her two siblings, and gave 22 to her mum for her Pavlova pudding. How many grapes did Ann start with?

A	B	C	D	E
24	44	30	22	54

13) Ben started with 15 tennis balls this season. He lost a few and was left with six. He gives half of his remaining balls to his cousin, and keeps three. How many balls did he lose?

A	B	C	D	E
9	6	12	10	8

14) Bill is 2 ½ times older than his son Louie. He is 50. How old is Louie?

A	B	C	D	E
27	18	20	25	32

15) If you treble Nisha's age and add 11, you have her mother's age of 50. How old is Nisha?

A	B	C	D	E
11	15	14	53	13

Glossary

BIDMAS:	Stands for brackets, indices, division, multiplication, addition and subtraction, i.e. the order in which a calculation is carried out.
Brackets:	Symbols that show those terms that should be treated together and calculated first, in the order of operations.
Capacity:	The measure of the space within a 3D object.
Continuous data:	Data that comes from measurement such as rainfall measurement.
Consecutive:	One number following the other continuously.
Cube number:	A cube number is a number which has been produced by another number and multiplied by itself and itself again. It is a whole number that has been raised to the power of 3.
Cumulative frequency:	A running sum of the frequencies.
Data:	Collective name for pieces of information, often used for reference or analysis.
Decimal place:	The position of a digit to the right of a decimal point.
Decimal point:	In a decimal number the decimal point separates the whole number from the part that is smaller than 1
Denominator:	The number at the bottom of a fraction.
Density:	The mass per unit volume of a solid.
Digit:	Any of the numerals from 0 to 9, especially when forming part of a number.
Discrete data:	Data that can be counted such as number of house points collected in a week.
Equation:	Has an equals sign in it, e.g. $3x + 1 = 7$
Estimate:	Roughly calculate or judge the value, number or quantity.
Exchange:	To 'borrow' in subtraction.
Expression:	A collection of terms or variables, e.g. $2x + 2y$ or $5r + 6$ without an equals sign.
Factor:	A number or quantity that when multiplied with another produces a given number or expression.
Formula:	A mathematical relationship or rule expressed in symbols. The plural is formulae.
Fraction:	A numerical quantity that is not a whole number.
Frequency:	The number of times an event occurs.
Frequency chart:	A table that shows the total for each category or group of data.
Imperial system:	A measuring system based on feet, gallons and pounds as units of length, capacity and weight or mass.
Index (power):	The index of a number says how many times to use the number in multiplication. It is written as a small number to the right and above the base number. In this example: $4^3 = 4 \times 4 \times 4 = 64$. The plural of index is indices.
Integer:	A whole number.
Intervals:	An interval is the distance between one number and the next on the scale of a graph.
Length:	The distance of the longest dimension of a shape.
Linear:	A straight line on a graph.
Line graph:	Graph formed by joining points together with straight lines.
Mass:	The weight of an object. A measure of how much matter is in an object. Mass is measured in grams and kilograms in the metric system and in pounds and stones in the imperial system.

Metric system:	The decimal measuring system based on the metre, litre and gram as units of length, capacity, and weight or mass. Converted in powers of 10
Multiples:	The numbers in multiplication tables, e.g. multiples of 3 are: 3, 6, 9, 12, etc.
Numerator:	The number above the line in a fraction showing how many parts.
Place value:	The numerical value that a digit has by virtue of its position in a number.
Power of:	The power of a number says how many times to use the number in a multiplication. It is written as a small number to the right and above the base number.
Prime number:	A number that only has two factors: itself and 1
Product:	The result when two numbers are multiplied together.
Quotient:	A result obtained by dividing one quantity by another.
Regroup:	Regrouping is often used in subtraction and addition. It is also known as 'carrying' and 'borrowing' numbers.
Rounding:	Alteration of a number to one less exact but more convenient for calculations.
Sequence:	A set of numbers containing a pattern.
Significant figures:	Each of the digits of a number that are used to express it to the required degree of accuracy, starting from the first non zero digit.
Square number:	A square number is a number that results from a number that has been multiplied by itself. It is a whole number that has been raised to the power of 2
Substitution:	The act of replacing a letter with a number or a number with a letter.
Tabulated:	To put information into a table format.
Tally chart:	A table with tally marks to show a valuable data set.
Term:	One of the parts of an expression or a number in a number sequence.
Triangular number:	Like square numbers which can be illustrated in a square pattern, you can illustrate triangular numbers in two types of triangle patterns.
Vertices:	A corner on a shape is referred to as a vertex. The plural is vertices.
Volume:	The amount of space that a substance or object occupies, or that is enclosed within a container.

Lesson 1: Place Value page 8

Develop page 9

1)
	A	600 million
	B	30 thousand
	C	700 or seven hundred
	D	$\frac{5}{10}$ or five tenths
	E	$\frac{6}{1000}$ or six thousandths
	F	$\frac{1}{1000000}$ or one millionth

2)   i)
   a)   3621.43
   b)   728.91

     ii)
   a)   462.38
   b)   2.3941

Lesson 2: Rounding Numbers page 10

Develop page 11

1)
   a) 86700
   b) 86734.29
   c) 86730
   d) 86734.3

2)
   a) 2864.4
   b) 3000
   c) 2900

3)
   a) 867
   b) 867.43
   c) 867

Answers

Timed Test 1 page 12

Question	Answer
1	D = 30000
2	B = 629416.5782
3	A = 3678.9
4	E = two thousandths
5	C = £29450
6	E = 130000
7	C = 23420 ft
8	A = 83.4 secs
9	C = 35000
10	D = 186500
11	A = 10000
12	B = 14000
13	E = 3500000
14	A = 605005027
15	E = 1hr 27m 32.5s

Lesson 3: Special Numbers and Number Sequences page 14

Develop page 17

1)	81	100	121	(square numbers)
2)	23	29	31	(prime numbers)
3)	100	81	64	(square numbers)
4)	8	64	216	(cube numbers)
5)	24	40	30	(alternate sequence)
6)	6	21	36	(triangular numbers)
7)	63	45	27	(9 × table)
8)	13	21	34	(Fibonacci sequence)
9)	159	319	639	(double the number and then add one)
10)	240	60	15	(divide by 2 each time)

Lesson 4: Addition and Subtraction page 18

Develop page 21

1) 353.12
2) 18.89
3) 1127.43
4) 21.33
5) 1013
6) 79.2
7) 6.993
8) 2978.002
9) 736.55
10) 1093.35

Timed Test 2 page 22

Question	Answer	Explanation
1	C = 310	142 goals + 168 goals = 310 goals
2	B = 2786L	6000L − 3214L = 2786L
3	A = 12.55m	9.75m + 2.8m = 12.55m
4	E = 341.69cm	87.91cm + 36.32 + 209.40cm + 8.06 = 341.69cm
5	D = 2750m	Convert 4km and 1.25km to 4000m and 1250m 4000m −1250m = 2750m
6	A = 8.811m	8.9m − 0.089m = 8.811m
7	B = 3.8km	31.5km + 6.9km = 38.4km 42.2km − 38.4km = 3.8 km
8	E = 5.84kg	2.5kg + 1.75kg + 2.25kg = 6.5kg − 0.66kg = 5.84 kg
9	E = 63.88kg	62.5kg + 60.32kg + 80kg + 83.3kg = 286.12kg 350kg − 286.12kg = 63.88kg
10	D = 29.5km	7.7km + 12.3km + 9.5km = 29.5kg
11	C = 7.5hrs	1hr (maths) + 1.5hr (gym) + 1.75hr (ice skating) + 3.25hr (athletics) = 7.5hrs
12	B = 9900m	10000m − 100m = 9900m
13	C = 163	201 − 38 = 163 photographs
14	D = 94	A pentagon has 5 sides, a rectangle has 4 sides, all triangles have 3 sides, an octagon has 8 sides $= (5 \times 3) + (2 \times 4) + (2 \times 3) + (3 \times 3) + (7 \times 8)$ $= (15 + 8 + 6 + 9) + (7 \times 8)$ $= 38 + 56$ $= 94$ sides
15	B = 105.4 miles	12.4 miles + 43.9 miles + 0.6 miles + 28.8 miles + 19.7 miles = 105.4 miles

Lesson 5: Multiplication page 24

Develop page 29

1) 600
2) 27000
3) 4.8
4) 0.24mm
5) 56.8
6) 6923.2
7) 91.648
8) 55.61
9) £671.50
10) 238.52

Timed Test 3 page 30

Question	Answer	Explanation
1	D = 1944	324 × 6 = 1944 oak trees
2	A = 4004	286 × 14 = 4004 performances
3	B = £408.50	86 × £4.75 = £408.50
4	E = 1488mm	32 × 46.5mm = 1488 mm
5	A = 3358	146 × 23 = 3358 passengers
6	C = 14580	324 × 45 = 14580 napkins
7	D = 20864	326 × 64 = 20864 pages
8	C = £1161	£21.50 × 3 × 18 = £1161
9	B = £664.64	£0.67 × 32 × 31 = £664.64
10	E = 5168	19 × 34 × 8 = 5168 words
11	C = 27864	43 × 216 × 3 = 27864 stitches
12	A = 72	(5 + 1) × (6 × 2) = 6 × 12 = 72 minutes
13	D = 21252	253 × 84 = 21252 passengers
14	A = £137.34	£1.09 × 42L × 3 = £137.34
15	B = £8250	(5 boxes × 6 year groups × 50 packets) × £5.50 = £8250

Lesson 6: Division page 32

Develop page 35

1) 35
2) 2839
3) 30615
4) 3421
5) 231
6) 142
7) 234
8) 321
9) 480
10) 562

Timed Test 4 page 36

Question	Answer	Explanation
1	B = 12p	£0.96 ÷ 8 = 12p
2	D = £0.25	6000p ÷ 24 = 25p
3	E = 36	1 packet = 15 rolls 540 ÷ 15 = 36 packets of ham
4	D = 25	1 week = 16 merit marks 400 ÷ 16 = 25 weeks
5	E = 15	255 ÷ 17 = 15 students
6	A = 20	500 ÷ 24 = 20 complete sheets
7	E = 25p	£3 ÷ 12 = 25p
8	D = 34	578 ÷ 17 = 34 nails
9	E = 5m	$6 \times 4 \times \square = 120$ 120 ÷ 24 = 5m
10	D = 28	700 seats ÷ 25 schools = 28 students per coach
11	B = 12	A square based pyramid has 5 vertices. 60 ÷ 5 = 12
12	D = 95	285 ÷ 3 = 95 children
13	A = 2341km	98322 ÷ 42 = 2341km
14	D = 512	$\frac{8}{30}$ of 1920. Therefore 1920 ÷ 30 = 64 64 × 8 = 512 sheep
15	C = 14	33 + 51 = 84 ÷ 3 = 28 28 ÷ 2 = 14 fish each per day on average

Lesson 7: Multiplying and Dividing by 10, 100 and 1000 page 38

Develop page 40

1)   73.4
2)   8920
3)   30
4)   0.8
5)   0.657
6)   0.005
7)   6.78
8)   0.0074
9)   2100
10)   800

Lesson 8: Order of Operations (BIDMAS) page 41

Develop page 42

1) $3 \times 16 = 48$
2) $30 \div 2 + 3 = 18$
3) $20 \div 4 = 5$
4) $7 + 4 = 11$
5) $4 + 6 = 10$
6) $3 \times (25 - 16) = 3 \times 9 = 27$
7) $40 \div 8 = 5$
8) $12 \div 4 = 3$
9) $2 + (8 \times 1) \times 4 = 2 + 8 \times 4 = 2 + 32 = 34$
10) $4 \times 64 = 256$

Try
i) $4 - 2 + 8 = 10$
ii) $5 + 4 \times 6 - 8 = 21$
iii) $2 + 6 \div 3 \times 4 = 10$
iv) $1 + (3 \times 8) \div 6 - 2 = 3$

Timed Test 5 page 43

Question	Answer	Explanation
1	C = £23.52	(14 × 8) × 0.21 = £23.52
2	A = 20	1 length = 15 seconds 5 min = 5 × 60 = 300 seconds 300 ÷ 15 = 20 lengths
3	E = 6	£24 × 1 + (8 × £12) £120 ÷ £20 = 6
4	B = 240	(5 × 4) × 12 = 20 × 12 = 240 claws
5	D = 136 secs	(8 × 60) + 23 = 503 seconds for Venus (6 × 60) + 7 = 367 seconds for Mars 503 − 367 = 136 seconds
6	E = 2.55L	Convert all bottles to ml. 300ml + 750ml + 1500ml = 2550 ml = 2.55 litres
7	A = £5354	£8.50 × 3hrs × 2 evenings per week × (52 weeks × 2 years) + £50 £51 × (104) + £50 = £5354
8	C = 332	(26 cabbages × 6 rows) + (8 lettuces × 18 rows) + 32 cauliflowers = 156 + 144 + 32 = 332 vegetables
9	A = 80	8 bottles × 750ml = 6000ml. 8 pineapples makes 600ml. So 10 times this number are needed to make 6000ml
10	E = 114L	2280L × 3 days = 6840 6840 ÷ 60 cows = 114 litres
11	B = £14	£1.75 − £1.25 = 50p profit per toy 50p × 28 toys = £14.00
12	C = 350	⅞ − ⅜ = ⅝ of the children attended school 560 ÷ 8 = 70 70 × 5 = 350 children
13	B = 25920	4 supermarkets × (36 crates × 180 jars) = 4 × 6480 = 25920 jars
14	A = 8	23 pages × 12 cards = 276 cards 284 − 276 = 8 cards
15	D = £110	£26 × 12 = £312 for total cost of lessons £85 + £117 = £202 currently saved £312 − £202 = £110 more to be saved

Lesson 9: Fractions page 46

Develop page 47

1) 36
2) 36
3) 88
4) 60
5) 42
6) 27
7) 120
8) 800
9) 2280
10) 2160

Timed Test 6 page 48

Question	Answer	Explanation
1	D = 80	$\frac{1}{5}$ of 100 = 20 golf balls. 100 − 20 = 80 golf balls
2	E = £4.90	$\frac{6}{7}$ is equal to £4.20. So $\frac{1}{7}$ is 70p. Adding £4.20 to 70p gives £4.90
3	A = $\frac{2}{5}$	Jack travels a total of 1200m to school there and back. 3km is equivalent to 3000m. So $\frac{1200}{3000}$ can be simplified to $\frac{2}{5}$
4	D = $\frac{2}{7}$	On a Tuesday and Wednesday, the baby would sleep 16 hours. The total for the week is 56 hours. $\frac{16}{56}$ in its lowest terms is $\frac{2}{7}$
5	D = $\frac{1}{5}$	5 litres is equivalent to 5000ml. The total amount in 4 bottles is 1000ml (4 × 250ml). $\frac{1000}{5000}$ can be simplified to $\frac{1}{5}$
6	B = $\frac{1}{5}$	The total number of animals on Bracken Farm is 95. There are 19 ducks and this is one fifth of the total ($\frac{1}{5}$)
7	B = $\frac{1}{8}$	Nigel spends 3 hours on the train every week day. 3 hours out of every 24 hours (full day) equates to $\frac{1}{8}$
8	B = 20	There are 18 thirds in 6. Add 18 to two thirds ($\frac{2}{3}$) and this equates to 20 thirds
9	A = $\frac{5}{8}$	Brian has $\frac{3}{4}$kg of liquorice which is equivalent to $\frac{6}{8}$kg. If he gives $\frac{1}{8}$ away this leaves $\frac{5}{8}$
10	C = £12	Jason spends $\frac{1}{3}$ of £45 on clothes which is £15. $\frac{2}{5}$ on stationery which is £18. £18 + £15 = £33. This is subtracted from £45 to leave £12
11	E = 48 miles	$\frac{3}{5}$ of 120 = 72, so Anita has already driven 72 miles. 120 subtract 72 leaves 48 miles left to drive
12	C = 360h	The farmer grows swedes on $\frac{4}{16}$ of 480 hectares which is 120 hectares. To find the hectares for the wheat the calculation is 480 − 120 = 360 hectares
13	A = 525	She checks a total of $\frac{5}{12}$ on days 1 and 2. $\frac{5}{12}$ of 900 components is 375. To find the amount left, 900 subtract 375 equals 525
14	B = £60	To find $\frac{6}{16}$ it is easier to simplify this fraction to $\frac{3}{8}$. $\frac{1}{8}$ equals £20. So to find $\frac{3}{8}$, multiply £20 by 3 to give £60
15	C = $\frac{4}{25}$	$\frac{80}{500}$ voted, other, and this can be simplified to $\frac{4}{25}$

Answers

Lesson 10: Decimals page 50

Develop page 51

1)	5.91
2)	14.62
3)	1.44
4)	9.1

5)	7.59
6)	20
7)	1.05
8)	135.88
9)	20.25
10)	14.08

Timed Test 7 page 52

Question	Answer	Explanation
1	E = 2.25	If you remove the decimal point it is 15 × 15 which is 225. Add the decimal point and it becomes 2.25
2	C = 0.18	To find the difference use the inverse operation. Add 0.08 to 0.02 to make 0.1 and then add 0.1. Therefore, 0.08 + 0.1 = 0.18
3	B = 11.8	To find the difference between the numbers round 38.2 to 40. This is 1.8. Then add 10 to 40. Therefore, 1.8 + 10 = 11.8
4	B = 3.33	When the whole numbers are reordered the middle (median) number is 3.33
5	A = 99.01	93.41 + 5.6 = 99.01
6	D = 5	You can say 'how many 1.2s in 6?' This question can be solved using repeated addition. 1.2 + 1.2 + 1.2 + 1.2 + 1.2 = 6 therefore 6/1.2 = 5
7	A = £10	If the pence amounts are added together they equal £1. The pounds total £9. So £1 + £9 = £10
8	B = 3.32m	Convert 152 into metres, which is 1.52m. Add together 1.45m + 1.52m + 0.35m = 3.32m
9	E = 7.9m	To find the average add together all the distances and divide by how many scores there are. 77.70 + 7.99 + 8.01 = 23.70/3 = 7.9
10	B = 11.1	Counting back 15 tenths can also be equivalent to subtracting 1.5. 12.6 − 1.5 = 11.1
11	B = 14	Use the inverse operation, 0.5 × ? = 7
12	C = 5	Use repeated addition or multiplication. 330ml × 5 = 1.650L
13	B = £27.44	Convert all the amounts into the same value, either pounds or pence, i.e. £0.88 + £8 + £0.80 + £8.08 + £8.88 + £0.80
14	A = 3L	Convert 100 cl to 1 litre and add all the numbers together. 1.2 + 1.0 + 0.8 = 3.0
15	D = 1.331	If you remove the decimal point it becomes 11 × 11 × 11 = 1331 Add the decimal point back in and it becomes 1.331

Lesson 11: Percentages page 54

Develop page 55

1)   8
2)   9
3)   24
4   70
5)   750
6)   2100
7)   15
8)   54
9)   34.5
10)   368

Timed Test 8 page 56

Question	Answer	Explanation
1	B = 196	2% of 200 is 4. 200 − 4 = 196
2	C = 70%	There are 420 fiction books (600 − 180). $\frac{420}{600}$ is equivalent to $\frac{7}{10}$. This is 70%.
3	D = £144	20% of £120 = £24. £120 + £24 = £144
4	B = 75%	$\frac{60}{80}$ is equivalent to ¾. ¾ = 75%
5	A = £120	25% is the same as ¼. ¼ of £160 is £40. £160 − £40 = £120
6	E = £345	15% of £300 is £45. £300 + £45 = £345
7	B = £5082	21% of £4200 = £882. £4200 + £882 = £5082
8	C = 240	25% of 320 = 80 beds. 320 − 80 = 240
9	B = £1872	4% of £1800 = £72. £1800 + £72 = £1872
10	B = £1045	5% of £1100 = £55. £1100 − £55 = £1045
11	E = £280	8% of £3500 = £280
12	C = 10%	£7.92 − £7.20 = £0.72. $\frac{72}{720}$ is equivalent to 10%
13	A = £4.95	10% of £4.50 = 45p. £4.50 + 45p = £4.95
14	B = 279	7% of 300 = 21. 300 − 21 = 279
15	C = 80%	450000 − 250000 = 200000. 200000 ÷ 250000 × 100 = 80

Lesson 12: The nth Term page 60

Develop page 61

1)   d $3n - 1$
2)   c $(n + 2)^2$
3)   d $n^2 - 3$
4)   3 $\frac{n}{2} + 1$
5)   38 $4 \times 10 - 2$
6)   20 $5^2 - 5$
7)   198 99×2
8)   57 $4 \times 15 - 3$
9)   10th term $n^2 = 100$
10)   Yes $6 \times 3 = 18 - 4 = 14$

Lesson 13: Introduction to Algebra page 62

Develop page 63

1)   M = 2
2)   t = 7
3)   w = 9
4)   y = 21
5)   H = 45
6) $5 + 6 = 11$
7) $3 \times 6 = 18$
8) $5 \times 6 \div 3 = 10$
9) $5 + 2 \times 6 + 10 = 27$
10) $6 \times 10 - 5 = 55$
11)   2d
12)   3c
13)   2k
14)   16
15)   3

Lesson 14: Solving Algebraic Equations page 64

Develop page 67

1)	$y = 6$	$2y = 12$	$y = 12 \div 2$
2)	$R = 8$	$5R = 40$	$R = 40 \div 5$
3)	$n = 3$	$14n = 22 + 20$	$14n = 42$ $\quad n = 42 \div 14$
4)	$M = 5$	$41 - 6 = 7M$	$35 \div 7$
5)	$W = 4$	$16W = 73 - 9$	$16W = 64$
6)	$R = 32$	$R \div 8 = 10 - 6$	$R \div 8 = 4$ $\quad R = 4 \times 8$
7)	$J = 56$	$J \div 7 = 3 + 5$	$J \div 7 = 8$ $\quad J = 7 \times 8$
8)	$T = 96$	$T \div 24 = 32 - 28$	$T \div 24 = 4$ $\quad T = 4 \times 24$
9)	$y = 2$	$7y - y = 1 + 11$	$6y = 12$ $\quad y = 12 \div 6$
10)	$x = 1$	$17x - 9x = 2 + 6$	$8x = 8$

Timed Test 9 page 68

Question	Answer	Explanation
1	$D = 126$	$5^3 + 1 = 126$ ($5 \times 5 \times 5 = 125$)
2	$A = 57$	$4 \times 15 - 3$
3	$E = 54$	$(8 + 10)3 = 18 \times 3 = 54$
4	$C = 4e$	$6 \times e - 2 \times e = = 6e - 2e = 4e$
5	$D = 3g + 2h$	$g + g + 2 \times h + g = 2g + 2h + g = 3g + 2h$
6	$C = 100$	$A \div 10 - 5 = 5$ $A \div 10 = 5 + 5$ $A \div 10 = 10$, so $A = 100$
7	$B = 100$	$x \div 2 - 16 = 34$ $x = 34 + 16 \times 2 = 100$
8	$D = £6.50$	$£4.20 + £2.30$
9	$A = 29$	$12 + (16 - 2) + B + 1 = 56$ $27 + B = 56$ $B = 56 - 27 = 29$
10	$E = 3$	$22 - (6 + 4 + 2 + 5 + 2) = 22 - 19 = 3$
11	$C = £32$	$4F + £60 + £7 = £195$ $£195 - £7 - £60 = 128 \div 4 = £32$
12	$B = 44$	$22 + (8 \times 2) + 6 = 44$
13	$A = 9$	$15 - 6 = 9$
14	$C = 20$	$50 \div 2.5 = 20$
15	$E = 13$	$(50 - 11) \div 3 = 13$

Fill in the tables below with your results from each of the Timed Tests. Each test is marked out of 15.

Colour the Progress Grid on the next page to see how well you have done.

	Timed Test 1	Timed Test 2	Timed Test 3
Score	/15	/15	/15

	Timed Test 4	Timed Test 5	Timed Test 6
Score	/15	/15	/15

	Timed Test 7	Timed Test 8	Timed Test 9
Score	/15	/15	/15

Colour the grids below with your total mark from each Timed Test to see how well you have done.

Timed Test 1

Timed Test 2

Timed Test 3

Timed Test 4

Timed Test 5

Timed Test 6

Timed Test 7

Timed Test 8

Timed Test 9

Read the statements below for some hints and tips.

0 – 7: Carefully re-read the 'Learn' section and try the 'Develop' questions again. When you feel confident, retry the timed test.

8 – 12: Good effort, make sure you learn from your mistakes. Review the answers of the questions that you have got wrong and understand the correct calculations for next time.

13 – 15: Well done, you have shown a secure understanding.

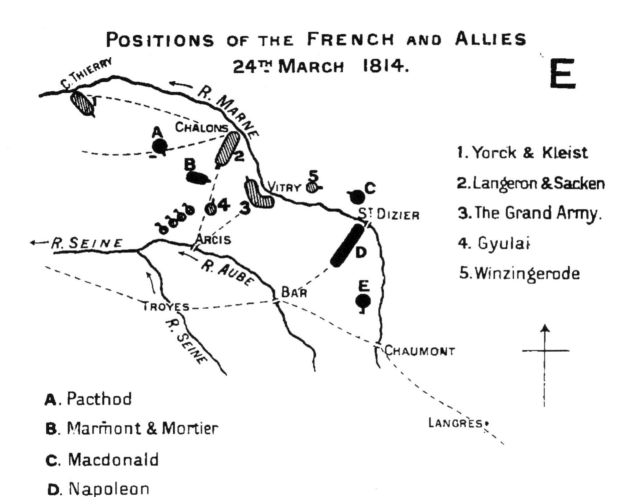

POSITIONS OF THE FRENCH AND ALLIES
24TH MARCH 1814.

E

1. Yorck & Kleist
2. Langeron & Sacken
3. The Grand Army.
4. Gyulai
5. Winzingerode

A. Pacthod
B. Marmont & Mortier
C. Macdonald
D. Napoleon
E. French Cavalry

Lightning Source UK Ltd.
Milton Keynes UK
UKHW051612200820
368550UK00014B/1660